to Nic Martinek

Foreword *- by David Ullendorff*

I MET LARRY IN 2001 through Peter Markovitz, my business partner and friend. Peter and I had been searching for the best math program in the world to serve as the brain and beating heart of our new venture, Mathnasium.

Our quest had taken us from education think tanks and the math departments at top universities, to the cutting edge of the educational technology industry. We were impressed with what we'd found, but something was still missing. We'd been searching for two years, and like the practical older sister in a Jane Austen novel, we needed to get married. It was time to make a responsible choice and commit. Falling in love with a math program would have to be put aside with other childhood fantasies. Then we met Larry.

In Los Angeles, Larry is known as "The Math Guy." There are legends about him coaxing un-teachable students out of their shells and kick-starting their brains into loving math; transforming leaden D's into golden A's like a medieval alchemist. I didn't believe a word of it.

Peter ushered me to the back of a classroom where Larry was training several middle school teachers. At first I didn't know what to make of the white beard and pony tail. The guy was either Merlin or driftwood left on the beach from the receding tide of the '60s. I gave Peter an Oliver Hardy "Here's another fine mess you've gotten us into" look, and settled in to listen.

The next 30 minutes turned what I thought I knew about teaching math upside-down. Colorful cartoon counting elephants aside, everything I had seen up to that point explained math in a way that made sense to teachers. The teachers then did their best to impart their understanding on to the students who, in their turn, memorized algorithms, times tables, and other math facts so that they got a good grade on the test. But with Larry, kids learned by heart — that is to say, fully invested with their entire beings. I don't expect you to believe this, but they fell in love with the subject.

Larry's approach was inside out: Teaching math in a way that made sense to kids. The teachers had to think like the children — the children didn't have to think like the teachers. So simple, yet so profound. It was a paradigm shift, like realizing that the earth revolves around the sun and not the other way round. Where the !&*@ was this guy when I was in school!?

While listening to Larry, I had to control the urge to run outside, grab some kid off the playground, and explain fractions to him in a way I knew he'd never heard before. After the session, I pushed past the phalanx of excited teachers and asked Larry how long it took him to develop his approach. The textbook curriculum you find in a school is manufactured by teams of instructional designers. They're expensive, and the publishers work them like galley slaves to get the books completed on time and under budget — a process that can take a year or a lot less for a cut-rate product.

It turned out that Larry had created his program over 30 years in the refiner's fire of the classroom by trying something, discarding it, and then trying something else until it worked; until it made sense to kids. Over three decades, he reimagined grade school math from the ground up, organizing it into new categories that served the subject and not politics, as is so often the case with state standards.

The beauty of Larry's system is that it is unified by three deceptively simple threads: Counting, Wholes and Parts, and Proportional Thinking. I know what you're thinking: Sounds good for elementary school, but what does that have to do with geometry, algebra, trigonometry, and calculus?

A great deal, it turns out. The bogeyman of geometry, corresponding parts of similar figures, is solved by Proportional Thinking. Integral calculus is an advanced form of Counting that enables you to get as close to infinity as possible. Wholes and Parts is the magic key to every word problem on the SAT, ACT, and GRE because this thread gives students the tools to freeze the action and lay bare the relationship between the elements of the problem..

Foreword cont'd

Kids that go through Larry's program leave with much more than A's. Math ceases to be an indomitable peak and becomes a steady friend that grows with you as you spiral around those deceptively simple threads, revisiting them grade after grade, until, over time, you've built a mental cathedral of interlocking math constructs that can support ideas of enormous complexity.

When I asked Larry what the scope and page count of the program was, he looked at me as if I had asked him how many strands of hair were braided into his pony tail. It turns out there were several thousand (pages of material, that is). I'm not sure of the exact number because he still keeps surprising me with new stuff.

I spent the summer at Larry's house, reading his work as he printed it out in stacks from any one of his five computers. The more I read, the more excited I became. Returning home at night, I would call Peter on my cell phone and, like a teenager, leave excited messages: "Peter, I think he's the one."

I also met Nic one day that summer when I took a break from the math and snooped around Larry's house, examining the myriad of books, art, and knick-knacks. Larry and his wife, Lynn, had told me that they lived alone, but there was obviously someone else in the house, and his stuff was everywhere: humorous paintings and sculptures; origami that got smaller and smaller like a Russian matryoshka doll; a number field — not $zn + a(n-1)z + ... + a = 0$ — but an actual landscape with numbers as flora and fauna.

Whoever this guy was, his signature was also all over the curriculum: the same humor and marriage of brevity and depth; one-half described as "two parts the same"; denominators, illustrated as apples and bananas, which have to be identical to be added because there is no such thing as a banapple.

Larry caught me examining a penguin made out of pistachio shells and told me about its creator, the other person in the house. Every magician has his secret. In Larry's case, it was Nic, his only son.

Nic was born five years into Larry's teaching career, when Larry was already deeply involved in changing secondary education through an appointment to the RISE Commission (Reform of Intermediate and Secondary Education). Larry had also begun to develop his own materials to use with gifted magnet schools, as well as gang diversion and inner-city programs.

Nic, a mathematically precocious child, gave his dad an inside look at the developing mind and led Larry to write his first book, "Math Tips for Parents." As Larry's career expanded from classroom teacher to school consultant extraordinaire and training expert, Nic was there, giving his dad's work an extra dimension. Who better to explain how children think than a child? Nic grew with his dad's body of work, contributing until the works of father and son were inseparable, wound together like strands of hair that form a braid.

Tragedy struck in May, 1999, when Nic died at age 19 in a car accident. Not long before the accident, Nic told Larry, "Dad, you have to show as many teachers as you can how to teach math the way you do." Nic had seen many of his friends leave high school unprepared in math — not because they couldn't handle the subject, but because they had not been taught in a way that made sense to them. They lacked that interlocking cathedral of math constructs.

After meeting Nic, my summer's work took on a new urgency. We organized Larry's enormous inventory, and that fall, we opened the first Mathnasium Learning Center in the Westwood neighborhood of Los Angeles.

Since then, Larry and Nic's work has taken on a life of its own. At this writing, there are over 170 Mathnasium Learning Centers internationally, with a new one opening every week. Together, the centers are helping schools and teachers — and most importantly, teaching kids math, one by one, in a way that makes sense to them.

This Math Dictionary is just one of the many gems I came across during that summer of 2002.

David Ullendorff
Mathnasium Co-Founder
March 6, 2007

"I LIKE COMING TO MATHNASIUM. I GET EDUCATED HERE."

- Overheard. (*5th grade student talking to his friend*)

"I LOVE MATH."

- Anonymous (*graffiti found on the wall of the Mathnasium Center in Los Angeles*)

"I HAVE AN ALGEBRA STUDENT NAMED HOLLY. WHEN SHE WALKED INTO THE CENTER A FEW MONTHS AGO, SHE WAS DRESSED 'DIFFERENTLY' (GOTH, ALL BLACK, HEAVY EYELINER) AND HAD A TOUGH-GIRL ATTITUDE. AFTER THE PRE-ALG ASSESSMENT, SHE WAS LITERALLY IN TEARS. AS I GOT TO KNOW HER, I REALIZED SHE WAS ACTUALLY QUITE MATURE FOR HER AGE AND FAR MORE CAPABLE THAN SHE GAVE HERSELF CREDIT FOR. TODAY, I NOTICED A QUOTE ON HER BINDER THAT READ, 'LOVE IS LIKE A MATH PROBLEM...YOU HAVE TO WORK AT IT BEFORE YOU GET IT RIGHT.' I ASKED HER WHERE SHE GOT THAT FROM, AND SHE SAID SHE CAME UP WITH IT (SO I PROMPTLY ASKED IF I COULD SHARE IT WITH YOU). I HAD TO SMILE TO MYSELF, KNOWING WE'VE BEEN ABLE TO STRIKE A CHORD WITH HER."

- Michael Sumida, *Mathnasium Center Director*

11:30

MA✗HNASIUM®
The Math Learning Center

Student: Mary Callan

Date: 7/14

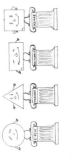

Today I worked on: Scientific Notation, Powers of 10,
Square Roots

One skill/concept I "GOT" today is: How to figure out square roots

One skill/concept I need to keep practicing is: Square roots

(signature)

Instructor's Signature

_____ Binder/Check in —Check Out
_____ Last Punch form – Time in
_____ Punch Card (10 cards = $15 GC, 1 card - Cabinet)
_____ Units of measure sheet; WOB: Yes or No
_____ **Code of Conduct** (Treat all with courtesy)

- ○ Quiet voices
- ○ Give instructors complete attention—headphones off
- ○ No cell phone use unless with parent
- ○ Raise hand for help
- ○ Don't interrupt an instructor working with another student

_____ Prescriptive—lollipop after 2 pages
_____ Focus on **your own** progress
_____ Rewards—Mastery check/shirts
_____ Nerd Award and 100 for 100%
_____ Introduce other instructors
_____ Color Binder
_____ Bathrooms/water/drinks ok/no food while working

"I HAVE A 5TH GRADER WHO STUMBLED THROUGH THE CHECKUP, DOING ALMOST ALL THE PROBLEMS BY COUNTING ON HER FINGERS. I STARTED HER IN WORKOUT BOOK A, AND IN JUST THREE VISITS SHE HAS STOPPED COUNTING ON HER FINGERS! WHEN WE WORK WITH TEN, SHE REFERS TO 'TEN' AS 'OUR FRIEND.' THE CONCEPT HAS WORKED WELL FOR HER AND MAY WORK WELL FOR OTHERS. EACH TIME SHE APPROACHES A PROBLEM, SHE TELLS ME THAT SHE HAS TO FIND HER FRIEND 'TEN' FIRST. TODAY, SHE ANSWERED AN ENTIRE WORKSHEET CORRECTLY WITHOUT USING ANY SCRATCH PAPER. I ASKED HER HOW SHE DID THE WORKSHEET SO WELL. HER REPLY WAS

'WOW! I WISH I'D BEEN TAUGHT THIS WAY BEFORE. IT'S LIKE BEING DEPRIVED OF OXYGEN.''

- 5th grade Mathnasium student

"ROSES ARE RED,
VIOLETS ARE BLUE,
I HATED MATH,
UNTIL I MET YOU."

- Marie, Mathnasium student

CONTENTS

CONTINUUM

DECADE

FORMULA GRAPH HEXAGON INCREASE

NUMERAL ORIGIN

RATIO

UNIT VARIABLE WIDTH ZERO

"KIDS SHOULD SAY, 'AH-HA,'

absolute value The distance a number is from zero.

Note that since absolute value is a distance, it is always either positive or zero; it is never a negative quantity.

acute angle An angle whose measure is greater than 0° and less than 90°.

addend Any of a group of numbers or quantities being added together to create a sum.

Of two numbers to be added together, the addend is the newly introduced number that is being added, as opposed to the previously existing one to which it is being added (the augend).

In $a + b = c$, b is the addend (a is the *augend*).

In $\begin{array}{r} a \\ + b \\ \hline c \end{array}$, b is the addend.

addition Counting how many all together. The process of forming a whole.

adjacent Next to.

algebra Generalized arithmetic.
See "**Branches of Mathematics**" in Appendix 2.

algebraic structure A system with objects and operations, and the properties and rules that govern those operations.

algorithm A step-by-step set of instructions for performing a given task.

altitude A line from a vertex that is perpendicular to the opposite side. A figure has as many altitudes as it does angles.

analysis The separation of a whole into parts for individual study.

angle The figure formed by two rays diverging from a common point.

approximation To come close to; be nearly the same as.

arc A segment of a circle, laid-off on the circumference.

area The amount of space inside a 2-D figure, measured in square units.

argument The object upon which a function or operation acts, that is, the value at which the expression describing the function is to be evaluated. This is another name for each element in the domain of the function.

arithmetic The process of changing (transforming) one number into another by using a given set of rules. The mathematics of integers, rational numbers, real numbers, and complex numbers under the operations of addition, subtraction, multiplication, and division, that is, *computation*.

Associative Property The law of mathematics that allows the independent grouping of elements in a problem.

Operations (such as addition and multiplication) are associative because the elements can be *grouped* in any order without affecting the result.

$$(a + b) + c = a + (b + c)$$
$$(1 + 2) + 3 = 1 + (2 + 3)$$
$$(a \cdot b) \cdot c = a \cdot (b \cdot c)$$
$$(2 \cdot 3) \cdot 4 = 2 \cdot (3 \cdot 4)$$

NOTE: Generally, subtraction and division are not associative. It does matter how we group when we subtract and divide (except in special cases).

$$(a - b) - c \neq a - (b - c)$$
$$(9 - 5) - 1 \neq 9 - (5 - 1)$$

$$(a \div b) \div c \neq a \div (b \div c)$$
$$(12 \div 4) \div 2 \neq 12 \div (4 \div 2)$$

TRY THE FLIPBOOK IMAGES TO SEE THE "DOIN' THE GEOMETRIC" DANCE!

augend A quantity to which an addend is added, that is, the quantity being augmented by an addend.

average (mean) A number that typifies a set of given numbers; the usual; the expected value of a given set of numbers; the "evening-out" of a given set of numbers to a single number.

axes Two or more mutually perpendicular lines, regarded as a frame of reference.

axioma Given; an assumption which is taken to be self-evident and true; a statement which cannot be proved to be true or false.

axiomatic system A system which includes self-evident truths; truths without proofs and from which further statements, or theorems, can be derived.

backward Directed or facing the rear.

Done in a manner or an order that is opposite to a previous occurrence.

base The *side* or *face* of a geometric figure to which an altitude is drawn.

The *number* that is raised to a power (an exponent).

The number that is raised to a power to generate the whole numbers of a number system. The base of the decimal system is 10; the base of the binary number system is 2.

benchmark numbers Numbers that are used to help make calculations and estimates.

between In an intermediate space, position, or time.

The numbers 0, $1/10$, $1/2$, 1, 10, 25, 50, and 100 are commonly-used benchmark numbers.

binary A system of numerical notation that has 2 rather than 10 as a base.

binary operation An operation that combines two objects of one type to form another object of the same type.

In a binary arithmetic operation, a **starting number** (the *operand*) is acted on by an *operation* ($+, -, \times, \div$) and a **second number** (the *operator*), producing a **result**.

We can say that a binary operation transforms one number into another by means of a given operation,

$$\text{operand } [+, -, x, \div] \text{ operator} = \text{result}$$

binomial Consisting of or relating to two *names* or *terms*. A polynomial with two terms.

In algebra, an expression consisting of two terms connected by a plus or minus sign, such as $a + 6$.

Compare with "trinomial."

bisect To cut or divide into two ***equal*** parts.

borrow In subtraction, to take a unit (tenths, ones, tens, hundreds...) from the next larger denomination in the minuend to make a number larger than the number to be subtracted.

box A container with four sides perpendicular to the base. Also called a rectangular solid.

box-and-whisker A graphic method for displaying data using the median, quartiles, and the maximum and minimum of the data points. A box-and-whisker plot displays where the data are spread out and where they are concentrated.

calculus A method of *calculation*, both *numeric* and *symbolic*. The mathematics of limits and infinitesimals.

capacity A measure of *volume*; the amount a container will hold.

carry In addition, to take a unit (ones, tens, hundreds...) to the next largest denomination in the addend because the sum in the current column exceeds 9.

cent- A root word meaning **hundred** (100).

center A point or place that is equidistant from the sides or outer boundaries of something; the middle.

century A 100-year interval of time. A group of 100 things.

chance The likelihood of something happening.

change To become different; to undergo *transformation*.

chord A line segment that connects two points on a circle.

The longest chord is the diameter, which passes through the center of the circle.

circle The set of points in a plane everywhere equidistant from a given fixed point, the center.

circuit A path which can be completely travelled back to the starting point without a change of direction.

circumference The distance around a circle; the perimeter of a circle.

class A set or group containing members regarded as having certain attributes or traits in common.

coefficient A number or symbol multiplying another number or symbol in an algebraic term. Usually, the number or letter multiplying a variable or group of variables.

census The count of a population. An essential statistic.

column One or more vertical sections lying side by side on a page and separated by a rule, blank space, or some other delimiter.

common fraction A number that can be written in the form $^a/_b$, where **a** and **b** are integers and $b \neq 0$. All decimal fractions that terminate or repeat can be written as common fractions.

commutative property The law of mathematics that allows the independence of the ordering of the elements in a problem. Operations (such as addition and multiplication) are commutative because the elements can be operated on in any order without affecting the result.

$$a + b = b + a$$
$$2 + 5 = 5 + 2$$

$$ab = ba$$
$$3 \cdot 4 = 4 \cdot 3$$

NOTE: Generally, subtraction and division are not commutative. It does matter in what order we subtract and divide (except in special cases).

$$a - b \neq b - a$$
$$10 - 5 \neq 5 - 10$$

$$a \div b \neq b \div a$$
$$7 \div 3 \neq 3 \div 7$$

compare To note the difference in *absolute* size of (by subtraction) or the difference in *relative* size of (by division).

compass A device for drawing circles or circular arcs and for making measurements.

complement "The rest of it." The quantity necessary to make a complete whole; the remaining part with respect to the whole.

complex number A number of the form **a** + **b***i*, where **a** and **b** are real numbers and *i* is the square root of negative one (-1); $i = \sqrt{-1}$.

composite number A number with three or more distinct factors.

compute To determine a number or quantity.

computer A device that computes, especially a programmable electronic machine that performs high-speed mathematical or logical operations or that assembles, stores, correlates, or otherwise processes information.

concept Something formed in the mind; a thought or notion.

cone A pyramid with a circular base.

congruence The state of having the same size and shape.

conjecture An inference drawn from observed patterns in many examples.

constant A quantity that does not change in value. A number, term, quantity, or mathematical object that is assumed to be fixed within the given context.

constant of variation A fixed number (a *constant*) that relates quantities being multiplied and/or divided.

In $xy = 12$, 12 is the constant of variation.

In $x/y = 6$ and $x = 6y$, 6 is the constant of variation.

In $xy/z = 3$ and $z = 3xy$, 3 is the constant of variation.

See "direct and indirect variation."

continuum A continuous series; a whole.

coordinates A set of one, two, or three numbers used to determine the position of a point in a 1-, 2-, or 3-D frame of reference.

coefficient of correlation A statistical measure that relates how well a set of data points can be modeled by a trend line.

cosine The trigonometric function that is defined as the ratio of the leg adjacent to an angle to the hypotenuse of a right angle.

counter example An example of a conditional statement in which the hypothesis is true and the conclusion is false.

Counting Determining "how many total." Arithmetic is the "art of counting."

curve fitting Plotting data and observing the pattern to predict trends.

counting The process of determining quantity (how many, how much).

couple Strictly speaking, two. In common usage, more than one and less than a few.

cube A rectangular solid with all equal sides.

cubed The raising of a quantity to the third power.

cubic units The units used to measure volume.

curve A line that deviates from straightness in a smooth, continuous fashion.

cycle An interval of time during which a regularly repeated event or sequence of events occurs.

cylinder A "soup can"; a 3-D solid with a round and parallel top and bottom.

decade A 10-year interval of time.

decimal Numbered or ordered in groups of 10. A number written using base 10. Relating to tens or tenths.

decimal fraction A base 10 number written with a decimal point to separate the whole numbers on the left from the fractions on the right.

All decimal fractions either *terminate*, *repeat*, or *continue* to *infinity without terminating or repeating*.

Decimal Number System The number system where each place is 10 times greater than the place to the right of it and 10 times smaller than the place to the left of it.

decimal point A dot written in a decimal number to indicate where the place values change from *whole numbers* to *decimal fractions*.

decrease To get less or smaller, as in number, amount, or intensity.

deductive A series of logical steps in which a conclusion is drawn by directly reasoning from a set of statements that are known or assumed to be true.

degree (of angle) A unit of angular measure equal to $1/360$ of a complete revolution.

degree (of temperature) A unit division of a temperature scale.

denomination The collective *name* of a group of similar things (apples, dogs, inches).

A subset of a larger set used to identify (or name) the particular subset. For example, with "coinage," the denominations are the names of the particular note or coins used by a particular country.

denominator "De name of da fraction."

The number of equal parts in the whole tells us the denomination, the name, of a common fraction.

The denominator is the "bottom" number in a common fraction.

dependent variable The variable in a function. Its value is *dependent* on the value of the independent variable.

depth The measurement or dimension downward, backward, or inward.

diagonal A line segment joining two nonadjacent vertices of a polygon.

> From the Latin *dia-* (across) and *-gon* (angle): literally, "across from angle to angle."

diagram A picture designed to demonstrate or explain how something works or to clarify the relationship between the parts of a whole.

diameter The distance across a circle. The chord of a circle that passes through the center.

dichotomy The division into two usually mutually exclusive parts.

difference The answer to a subtraction question.

digit Any one of the ten Hindu-Arabic symbols:
$$0, 1, 2, 3, 4, 5, 6, 7, 8, 9.$$

In general, any numeric symbol less than the base of the number system.

dilation A transformation that either enlarges or reduces a geometric figure proportionately.

dimension A measure of space, especially width, height, or length.

direct proof A conclusion proved through deductive reasoning.

direct variation When one of two quantities changes, the other changes so that the ratio of the two quantities remains constant.

> As one quantity gets LARGER, another quantity gets LARGER, in the same proportion. [The more you work, the more money you earn (at the same hourly rate).]

> As one quantity gets SMALLER, another quantity gets SMALLER, in the same proportion. [The less you buy, the less you spend (on the same item).]

The equation of direct variation is $\frac{y}{x} = k$, which is also written as $y = kx$. Note that the equation of direct variation is a *straight line* that passes through the origin with slope k.

See "indirect variation."

direction The angular position of two points with respect to each other.

direction (of change) To the RIGHT usually denotes a POSITIVE change. To the LEFT usually denotes a NEGATIVE change.

discipline Instruction, teaching, learning, knowledge.

discount The amount deducted or subtracted from a cost or price.

discrete math The study of the properties of mathematical systems that have only a finite number of elements.

THE POWER OF 10

Ten is the base of our number system, most probably because we have 10 fingers on which to count things.

"Thinking in 10s," that is, understanding how the Decimal System really works, is something that comes naturally to some people and not to others. For those who have to work at it, and as continuing reinforcement for those who understand it right away, the school curriculum must be enhanced to provide a wide range of coordinated activities that will help students learn to deal with the many facets of 10.

distance Distance is the amount of space between two points, measured along a given pathway. Distance is measured in linear units. Distance is always either positive or zero.

distributive property The mathematical property that states:

"The product of the sum" is equal to "the sum of the products."

$$a(b + c) = ab + ac$$
$$3(4 + 5) = 3 \cdot 4 + 3 \cdot 5$$
$$(b + c)a = b\,a + ca$$
$$(2 + 3)5 = 2 \cdot 5 + 3 \cdot 5$$

"The product of the difference" is equal to "the differences of the products."

$$a(b - c) = ab - ac$$
$$2(8 - 3) = 2 \cdot 8 - 2 \cdot 3$$
$$(b - c)a = ba - ca$$
$$(5 - 3)4 = 5 \cdot 4 - 3 \cdot 4$$

"The quotient of the sum" is equal to "the sum of the quotients."

$$(b + c) \div a = b \div a + c \div a$$
$$(6 + 8) \div 2 = 6 \div 2 + 8 \div 2$$

"The quotient of the difference" is equal to "the differences of the quotients."

$$(b - c) \div a = b \div a - c \div a$$
$$(15 - 12) \div 3 = 15 \div 3 - 12 \div 3$$

THE MAIN IDEA OF THE DISTRIBUTIVE PROPERTY

Operating on the *whole* gives the same answer as operating on the *parts individually*.

dividend The number being *divided* into.
In $a \div b = c$, **a** is the *dividend.*

In fraction form, the *dividend* is the numerator.
In $^a/b = c$, **a** is *the dividend.*

division Counting "how many of *these* are there inside of *that.*"

The process of separating a whole into equal parts. Division is repeated subtraction. In "how many of *these* are inside of *that*," the divisor is the *these*, and the dividend is the *that*.

divisor The number we are dividing by.
In $a \div b = c$, b is the divisor.
In fraction form, the divisor is the denominator.
In $a/b = c$, b is the divisor.

dodecahedron A polyhedron with 12 faces.

dollar The basic unit of currency in many countries, including the United States. In the United States, a dollar equals 100 cents.

domain (of a function) The domain is the set of all possible values of the *independent variable* (the argument) of a function.

The domain is the set of all objects that are about to be acted on by the function.

See "argument."

double Composed of two like parts. Two times as many or as much.

"12" & "16" - THE IDEAL NUMBERS

Twelve is an ideal model of Fractional Parts because it can be divided into more fractional parts than any other small number, as follows:

1:1 group of 12 (1):2 groups of 6 ($1/2$):3 groups of 4, ($1/3$):
4 groups of 3 ($1/4$):6 groups of 2, and ($1/6$):12 groups of 1, ($1/12$.)

Many familiar systems, all separable into fractional parts, use 12. For instance, there are:

12 items in a dozen, 12 months in a year, 12 hours on the face of a clock, 12 inches in a foot, and 12 signs of the Zodiac.

There are 16 ounces in a pound because 16 is a small number that can be repeatedly cut in half and have whole number answers (16, 8, 4, 2, 1).

each One of a group considered individually.

element A basic part of a composite entity.
A single member of a set.

ellipse An oval. The set of points for which the sum of the distances from each point to two fixed points is equal.

empirical Relating to the collection of actual, perceived data.

equal Being the same in value.

equation A statement that two quantities (two mathematical objects) are equal.

equidistant The property of being the same distance from a given reference point, line, or other object.

equilateral triangle A triangle with three equal sides (and hence three equal angles).

estimation Determining or calculating an approximate amount, value, or size of something.

Euclidean Transformation In geometry, the process of changing one configuration into another, including slides, rotations, and reflections.

even No "left-overs"; no variations or fluctuations.

even number Exactly divisible by 2. Note that 0 is an even number because 0 divided by 2 has no remainder.

event One or more of the outcomes of a probability experiment.

E

example One entity that is representative of a group as a whole.

exponent The power to which a base is raised.

exponential function A function commonly used to study growth and decay. It has the form of $y = a^x$.

expression A mathematical phrase with no equality or inequality sign.

exterior Outside of. The surface of a geometric solid.

F

face Any of the flat sides of a polyhedron.

factor One of two or more quantities that divides a given quantity without a remainder.

One of the numbers that make up a number by multiplication.

> In $3 \times 4 = 12$, 3 and 4 are *factors* of 12 because they *multiply together* to make 12 and they *divide* evenly into 12. 1, 2, 6, and 12 are also factors of 12.

Any of two or more quantities that are multiplied together.

family A group of related quantities or entities.

finite Possible to reach or exceed by counting. Having bounds; limited.

finite graph A structure consisting of vertices and edges, where the edges indicate a mapping among the vertices (e.g., the vertices may represent players in a tournament, and the edges indicate who plays whom).

flip A transformation, also called a reflection, that produces a mirror image of a geometric figure.

for each Counting an item a certain number of times based on the amount of another quantity.

formula An equation that shows the relationship between a group of variables.

forward Directed or facing toward the front.

fourths A whole cut into four equal parts. One of the four equal parts. Half of a half.

fractal An algebraically generated complex geometric shape having the property of being endlessly self-similar under magnification.

fraction The result of breaking a whole into equal parts; one or more of those equal parts.

(Compare with "**division**.")

full circle 360°.

function A transformation where the values of one variable are determined by the values of another variable.

A relationship between two sets of numbers, the inputs and outputs, or the domain and range, in which each input leads to *exactly one* output.

function machine A way of visualizing how functions operate on inputs and produce outputs.

An **input number** goes into the function machine, it is *operated* on by the **function rule**, and an **output number** is produced at the other end.

A function machine transforms one number into another, according to a prescribed set of rules.

TORUS

Golden Ratio ø = $(1 + \sqrt{5})/2 \approx 1.618...$

See "phi."

Golden Rectangle A rectangle whose sides are in the Golden Ratio.

A rectangle is a Golden Rectangle when the ratio of the *length plus the width* to the *length* equals the ratio of the *length* to the *width*.

$$\frac{l + w}{l} = \frac{l}{w}$$

Golden Section A line is cut into a Golden Section when the ratio of the entire line to the longer of the two pieces equals the ratio of the longer piece to the shorter piece.

$$\frac{l + s}{l} = \frac{l}{s}$$

googol A word for the number 10^{100} (a "1" followed by one hundred 0s).

Supposedly based on a child's nickname for this number.

googolplex The number 10 to the googol power.

graph A diagram that shows the relationship between two quantities.

greater than A statement that one quantity is larger in size than another quantity.

Greatest Common Factor (GCF) The largest number that will divide evenly into each of a group of numbers.

group One or more of the same thing (1 apple, 9 dogs, 5 inches, 8 things).

half The first fraction. A whole divided into two equal parts; one of those parts.

"Two parts the same."

height In a geometric figure, the perpendicular distance from a vertex to its base.

hexagon A six-sided plane figure.

horizontal Parallel to the horizon; at right angles to a vertical line.

hypotenuse The side of a right triangle that is opposite to the right angle. It is always the longest side of a right triangle.

I
i

i The positive solution of the equation $x^2 = {}^-1$, i.e., the $\sqrt{{}^-1}$.

Identity Element The operator that leaves a given operand unchanged. The element that has no effect on other elements under a binary operation.

Zero is the Identity Element for addition and subtraction.

$$[\,a + 0 = a\,] \quad [\,a - 0 = a\,]$$

One is the Identity Element for multiplication and division.

$$[\,a \cdot 1 = a\,] \quad [\,a \div 1 = a\,]$$

identity property The mathematical property that for every operation (addition, subtraction, multiplication, division) there is an operator (the *Identity Element*) that leaves the operand unchanged.

imaginary number The square root of a negative number, usually expressed using *i*.

improper fraction A fraction whose value is greater than one whole. The numerator is necessarily greater than the denominator.

increase To become greater or larger, as in number, amount, or intensity.

increment A (usually) small addition or increase.

independent variable The input variable in a function. Its value may be chosen *independently* from within the domain of the function.

indirect proof A deductive proof using contradiction or elimination to rule out all cases except the desired conclusion.

indirect variation When one of two quantities changes, the other changes so that the *product* of the two quantities remains constant.

> As one quantity gets LARGER, another quantity gets SMALLER in the same proportion. [The more the number of workers, the less time the job takes (at the same rate of work).]

> As one quantity gets SMALLER, another quantity gets LARGER. [The less hours you work, the more you must be paid per hour to earn the same amount.]

The equation of indirect variation is $xy = k$. Note that the equation of indirect variation is *not* a straight line; it is a *hyperbola*.

See "direct variation."

inequality The statement that one quantity is less than or greater than another quantity.

inductive reasoning A form of reasoning from individual cases to general ones or from observed instances to unobserved ones.

inequality A statement indicating that two quantities are not equal, using symbols > (greater than) or < (less than) or ≠ (not equal to).

PLANE

infinite Impossible to reach or exceed by counting.

Having no boundaries or limits. Immeasurably large. Larger than any fixed finite quantity.

infinitesimal An immeasurably small amount or quantity.

infinity An indefinitely large number or quantity. Unbounded. A number larger than any bounded quantity.

input value The operator in a binary operation; the number that is operated on; the independent variable.

integer A positive or negative *Whole Number*, including 0. A member of the set {...-3, -2, -1, 0, 1, 2, 3...}.

A complete unit or entity.

interior Inside of.

intersection The set of points where one entity crosses another. In Set Theory, the intersection of two or more sets is the set that contains the elements that are common to *all* of the sets.

interval The distance from one number (or unit) to another. The space between two numbers.

A measurement of the separation of two values.

DOME
(HEMISPHERE)

inverse operation The operation that "undoes" the original operation.

Addition and *subtraction* are *inverse* (opposite) operations. *Multiplication* and *division* are *inverse* (opposite) operations.

Inverse Property The mathematical property that, for every operation (addition, subtraction, multiplication, division), there is an operator and an operand whose result under the operation is the Identity Element.

$$a + 0 = a \quad \text{Zero is the Identity Element}$$
$$a - 0 = a \quad \text{for addition and subtraction.}$$

$$a \cdot 1 = a \quad \text{One is the Identity}$$
$$a \div 1 = a \quad \text{Element for multiplication and division.}$$

$$a + \text{-}a = 0 \quad \text{Every number plus its opposite is } 0.$$
$$a \cdot {}^1/_a = 1 \quad \text{Every number times its reciprocal is } 1.$$

irrational number A number that cannot be written as a common fraction. Every irrational number can be written as a non-repeating, nonterminating decimal.

isosceles triangle A triangle with two equal sides (and hence two equal angles).

iterate To repeat an algorithm, using the previous output as the next input.

joint variation When a quantity varies DIRECTLY to another quantity and INDIRECTLY (INVERSELY) to another, it is said to vary JOINTLY with respect to both.

In $a = {}^{kb}/_c$,

a varies *DIRECTLY* to b and *INDIRECTLY* to c.

law A general principle or rule that is assumed or that has been proven to hold between various quantities.

Law of SAMEness It is only possible to add and subtract things of the *same* kind, things with the same *name*, the same *denomination*.

It is true that:

2 **apples** + 3 **apples** = 5 **apples** and

2 **b an an a s** + 3 **b an an a s** = 5 **b an an a s**,

but

2 **a pp l e s** + 3 **b an an a s** ≠ 5 **b an app l e s**.

Also,

2 apples + 3 bananas = 5 pieces of fruit
(a common denomination).

Least Common Multiple (LCM) The smallest number that a given group of numbers will divide into evenly.

leg Either of the two sides of a right triangle that is *not* the hypotenuse.

length The measurement of something along its greatest dimension.

less A smaller quantity. The act of "taking away."

less than A statement that one quantity is smaller in size than another quantity.

limit The point beyond which something cannot proceed.

In Calculus, a number or point **k** that is approached by a function $f(\mathbf{x})$ as **x** approaches **a** if, for every positive number e, there exists a number d such that

$$|f(\mathbf{x}) - \mathbf{k}| < e \text{ if } 0 < |\mathbf{x} - \mathbf{a}| < d.$$

line The path traced by a moving point. A line has zero thickness and infinite length. A line has "no beginning and no end."

line segment see "segment."

linear measurement Having only one dimension.

linear function A function with the characteristic that $f(x + y) = f(x) + f(y)$. [The *function of the sum* equals *the sum of the functions*.]

linear units Units that measure 1-D quantities.

locus The set of points that satisfy a given set of conditions.

logarithm An alternative notation for expressing an exponent.

logic A system of reasoning used to validate arguments.

GEOMETRY

Fun Facts about GEOMETRY:

- Every SQUARE is a RECTANGLE, but not every RECTANGLE is a SQUARE.

- The angles of any triangle add-up to $180°$.

- A STRAIGHT LINE is two right angles. A FULL CIRCLE is four right angles.

- There is no such thing as a "left angle."

magnitude The "size" of a number.
See "absolute value."

manipulative A physical object that is used
to teach an abstract idea in mathematics.

mathematics The study of wholes and parts,
and the relationship between them.

Moving objects, according to rules.

mathesis Science, learning; mental discipline,
especially, mathematics (L). "That which is learnt."

"mathing" The activity of actively doing math
(mentally, verbally, visually, kinesthetically, and in
writing). From the infinitive "to math" (coined
by Larry). As Larry sez, "Kids need to learn to
math just as they need to learn to read."

maths British spelling of "math."

matrix Literally "mother" (L). That which gives
form, origin, or foundation to something
enclosed or embedded in it. A place of origin
and growth. Related words include environment,
framework, womb, structure, model, enclosed,
enveloping, surrounding.

mean See "average."

measurement The determining of a quantity
using standard units to state the dimensions
of something.

measure of central tendency A number that
represents the "center" or "trend" of a set of
data. The mean, median, and mode are statistical
measures of central tendency.

median The middle number in a ranked set of data.

meter The international standard unit of length,
approximately equivalent to **39.37** inches.

A meter was originally defined as one-ten-mil-
lionth the distance from the North Pole to the
South Pole along the Prime Meridian (through
Greenwich, England).

It was redefined in **1983** as the distance travelled
by light in a vacuum in $1/299{,}792{,}458$ of a second.

ACUTE
ANGLE

ELLIPSOID

The Metric System The international standard for measuring *mass* (weight) [grams], *distance* [meters], and *capacity* [liters].

When going from a *smaller* unit to a *larger* unit, each unit of measure is 10 times *greater* than the previous unit.

When going from a *larger* unit to a *smaller* unit, each unit of measure is 10 times *smaller* than the previous unit.

middle Equidistant from the beginning and the end.

millennium A 1,000-year interval of time.

minuend The quantity *from which* something is being subtracted.

> In a − b = c, a is the minuend.

minus Another name for *subtraction*.

mixed number A "mixture" of a whole number and a proper fraction. The value of a mixed number is always greater than one whole.

mode The number that occurs the most often in a set of data.

model A pattern. An original used as an archetype.

modulus A constant factor by which we can change a thing from one name to another (from one system to another).

A constant or coefficient that expresses numerically the degree to which a property is possessed.

> From *modus* = measure

monad The one composed of the many. A collective singular for a group of related objects.

monomial An algebraic expression containing exactly one term.

The one term can be a *number*, a variable (with or without an exponent), or the product of a *number* and one or more variables.

more A greater or additional quantity.

multiple A number that can be divided by another number with no remainder.

multiplicand In a multiplication problem **ab = c**, the number **a** that is to be multiplied by the multiplier, **b**.

multiplication Counting "in equal groups." The process of forming a whole from equal groups.

Multiplication is repeated addition.

multiplier In a multiplication problem **ab = c**, the number **b** by which the multiplicand **a** is to be multiplied.

MMMMMM.... PIE
Fun Facts about π

- The trillionth digit of π is 9.

- Englishman William Oughtred, in 1647, was the first person to get really tired of writing 3.141592653...and started using the symbol π (Greek letter pi). It is unknown whether this was intentionally the greatest pun in history. It is known that he was fond of cherry pies.

name A name is a unique identifier.

Until the first division, there is only **1**. This doesn't really need a name. After the first division, there are now **2**, hence the need for a name.

natural number A member of the set {**1**, **2**, **3**...}; the Whole Numbers (excluding **0**).

negative (quantity) A quantity whose value is less than zero.

"No Choice" aka "Sherlock Holmes logic."

If **p** or **q** is a true statement, and we know **p** is false, we have "no choice" but to conclude that **q** is true.

non- A prefix meaning not; nullifying.

normal curve In statistics, the distribution of data along a bell-shaped curve that reaches its maximum height at the mean.

not The *negation* of.

number Something that expresses the "amount of or lack of."

numeral A symbol or mark used to represent a number.

numerator The number of parts of the whole being considered.

The numerator is the "top" number in a common fraction.

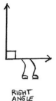

RIGHT
ANGLE

object A discrete item that can be selected, maneuvered, and manipulated, such as an onscreen graphic, a mathematical symbol or quantity, or physical item.

Something intelligible or perceptible by the mind.

Anything that can be transformed from one state into another.

From Latin *obiectum*, "thing put before the mind."

obtuse angle An angle whose measure is greater than $90°$ and less than $180°$.

obtuse triangle A triangle with an obtuse angle.

odd An integer that is not divisible by two. Odd numbers have a remainder of one when divided by two.

odds The ratio of the number of ways to win to the number of ways to lose.

of Used to indicate the Aggregate or Whole that includes the Part or Quantity denoted by the preceding word.

> most **of** the Class, *half* **of** a Pizza,
> *some* **of** the Time...

The mathematical operation associated with **of** is multiplication.

$$^3/_4 \text{ of } 20 = {}^3/_4 \times 20 = 15$$
$$7\% \text{ of } 490 = 0.07 \times 490 = 34.3$$

operand A quantity on which an operation is performed.

operation A process, such as addition, substitution, or transposition, performed according to specified rules.

operator A quantity which is operating on a given number.

SPHERE

opposite (from) Located directly across from something else.

opposite (of) The number with the *same* absolute value and *different sign*. The opposite of a positive number is a negative number, and the opposite of a negative number is a positive number.

opposites (additive inverse) Numbers with the same absolute value and opposite signs. Two numbers whose sum is 0.

opsimath One who starts learning late in life. A "late bloomer."

order A system of organization that prescribes what comes next.

order of operations The order in which operations are to be performed in a given problem.

PLEASE EXCUSE MY DEAR AUNT SALLY,
AND LET HER REST.

Parenthesis, Exponents,
Multiplication and Division (FROM LEFT TO RIGHT),
Addition and Subtraction (FROM LEFT TO RIGHT).

origin The point on a number line with the coordinate (0).

The point in a coordinate plane with coordinates (0, 0).

The point in a coordinate space with coordinates (0, 0, 0).

out of A phrase used to tell *how many* of a given group of things are currently being considered. "He made 3 out of 4 free throws."

output value The *result* of a binary operation. The independent variable.

pair One object composed of two similar things.

palindrome A number or other object whose digits (elements) read the same forward and backward.

parabola A U-shaped curve generated by a quadratic equation.

A plane curve formed by the locus of points equidistant from a fixed line and a fixed point not on the line.

paradigm An example that serves as a pattern or model.

parallel lines Coplanar lines that "never meet."

Note: This definition is fine except for those students who will be seriously pursuing math beyond high school. For them, the "everywhere equidistant" (see below) rather than "non-intersecting" view is preferable.

Two things are said to be parallel when they are "everywhere equidistant," always the same distance apart.

Always equidistant means that the two objects never intersect (never cross each other), except in the case where they are zero distance apart. *This means that objects can be parallel to themselves.*

parallelogram A quadrilateral with two sets of parallel sides.

parameter A "constant" variable quantity or value.

A quantity that is used in a relationship involving several quantities and is held fixed but in general may be allowed to have different values.

P

part A component of the whole. A fragment, fraction, section, portion, region; a piece broken off.

- Portion or division of a whole.
- That which together with others makes up a whole (whether really separate from the rest or, more often, only separated in thought).
- An aliquot part, exact divisor, submultiple.
- Factor.
- Any of several equal portions, quantities, numbers, pieces, etc., of which something is composed or into which it can be divided.
- A portion detached or cut from a whole; a fragment; a piece.
- A certain amount but not all: less than a whole.

pattern In a set of numbers, a rule for being able to figure out what number comes next.

A plan or model used to make things.

pentagon A five-sided plane figure.

per "For each." According to; by.

percent Literally, "for each 100," "parts per hundred," "how many for each hundred." The ratio of a number to 100.

(The) Percent Equation The Percent Equation states:

[Percentage Rate] x [Whole] = [Part]

percent of change The percent by which a number changes from an original value.

perfect cube The third power of an integer. 0, 1, 8, 27, 64, 125... are perfect cubes.

perfect square The second power of an integer. 0, 1, 4, 9, 16, 25... are perfect squares.

perimeter The distance around a geometric shape.

permutation An ordered arrangement of a finite number of items in a set.

perpendicular lines Lines that meet in a right angle.

OBTUSE ANGLE

phi (ø) The number of the Golden Ratio.
[See "Golden Ratio."]

Phi is an irrational number. Its decimal expansion begins with $1.618...$

philomath A lover of knowledge.

pi (π) The ratio of the circumference of a circle to its diameter.

The distance around a circle divided by the distance across is always the same number, namely, π.

Pi is an irrational number. Its decimal expansion begins with $3.141592653...$

place value The value of the position of a digit in a numeral. Place values are determined as powers of 10, starting at the decimal point.

The 1s place (10^0) is immediately before the decimal point, and the other places are determined as positive integral powers of 10 to the left of the decimal point, and negative integral powers of 10 to the right of the decimal point.

placeholder A symbol in an expression that may be replaced by any element of the set.

plane A flat surface that, in theory, extends infinitely in two directions.

A surface **S** with the property that a straight line joining any two points of **S** is also contained in **S**.

plus Another name for addition.

point A location in space. A point is 0-D. It has no length, width, or depth.

ICOSADODECA-
HEDRON

polygon A 2-D figure made up of sides of any length.

polyhedron A solid bounded by polygons; a 3-D object that has polygons as its faces.

polymath One who has knowledge of many subjects.

polynomial Consisting of one or more names or terms.

An algebraic expression consisting of one or more terms connected by plus or minus signs. Each term is made of a constant multiplier (the coefficient) and one or more variables raised to a power.

$$3x - 1, \quad 2x + 3xy, \quad 3xy - 2 \text{ are polynomials.}$$

portion A section or quantity within a larger thing; a part of a whole.

position A place or location.

positive (quantity) A quantity whose value is greater than zero.

power The value of a number raised to some exponent.

prime factor A factor of a given number that is itself prime.

prime number A number that has exactly two distinct factors, namely, 1 and *itself*.

Note that this definition precludes 1 from being a prime number because "1 and itself" are not distinct numbers.

Also, 2 is the only even prime number.

prime twins Two prime numbers that differ by 2. 11 and 13 are prime twins, as are 59 and 61.

prism A solid figure whose bases have the same size and shape and are parallel to one another, and each of whose sides is a parallelogram.

probability The likelihood (the chance) that a given event will occur.

Probability is the ratio of "the number of ways to win" to "the total number of ways things can happen."

product The answer to a *multiplication* question.

In $ab = c$, c is the product.

proper fraction A fraction whose value is less than one whole. The numerator is necessarily less than the denominator.

proportion Literally "according to amount." The multiplicative relation of one part to another or to the whole; relative size.

A part, share, or portion, especially in its relation to the whole; a quota.

Comparison, analogy, balance, symmetry.

The comparative relation between parts or things with respect to size.

An equation stating that two ratios are equal.

proportional In proportion.

proportional thinking Reasoning in groups

protractor A semicircular instrument for measuring and constructing angles.

pyramid A solid figure with a polygonal base and triangular faces that meet at a common point.

Pythagorean Theorem The statement that "the sum of the squares of the legs of a right triangle equals the square of the hypotenuse."

$a^2 + b^2 = c^2$, where a and b are *legs* of a right triangle and c is the *hypotenuse*.

quadratic function A function that has an equation of the form $y = ax^2 + bx + c$ where **a** does not equal 0.

quadrilateral A four-sided plane figure.

quantity A single term or collection of terms and operators considered as a single entity. "The one composed of the many."

> $(3ab)$, $(2 + 3a)$, $(5xy^2 + 2x + 4)$, and $(2[3x + (4x^2 - 5y)^2])$ are examples of quantities. A quantity may be as simple or complex as you wish.

The amount of something.

quarter One of four equal parts. Half of a half.

quotient The answer to a division question.

> In $a \div b = c$, **c** is the quotient.

R

radian The size of the central angle of a circle when the arc length equals the radius.

radius A line segment that joins the center of a circle with any point on its circumference. The plural is radii.

The distance from the center of a circle to any point on the circle.

random Having no specific pattern.

random variable A quantity that is unpredictable.

range (of a function) The range is the set of all the possible values of the *dependent variable*.

The range is the set of results of the function operating on the elements in the domain.

rate Describes how much one variable *changes* in relation to another.

A quotient used to compare two measures in different units.

A measure of a part with respect to a whole; a ratio.

STRAIGHT
ANGLE

ratio A comparison of two numbers by division.

A quotient used to compare two or more quantities of the same units of measure.

A statement of the relative size of two quantities (numbers, functions, and so on), expressed as a quotient.

A ratio tells us *how many times* bigger or smaller one number is than another.

> $\frac{12}{4} = 3$ says, "12 is 3 times as big as 4."
> $\frac{4}{12} = \frac{1}{3}$ says, "4 is $\frac{1}{3}$ times as big as 12."

ray A straight line extending from a point forever.

A ray has a "definite beginning and no end."

rational number Any number that can be written as a common fraction. Every rational number can be written as a repeating or terminating decimal.

More formally, a number of the form a/b, where **a** and **b** are integers and $b \neq 0$.

ray A straight line extending from a point.

real number The union of the set of rational numbers with the set of irrational numbers.

reciprocal For a given number **N**, $1/N$ is its *reciprocal*. When *reciprocals* are multiplied together, their product is **1**.

A *reciprocal* can be quickly found for any number by switching the numerator and denominator.

rectangle A quadrilateral with four right angles.

rectangular array An organized arrangement of square units (EXAMPLE: tiles).

rectangular solid A prism with a rectangular base. A box.

recurrence relation In finite math, a value in a series derived by applying a formula to the previous value.

recursive sequence In finite math, a series of numbers in which values are derived by applying a formula to the previous value.

reflection The mirror image of an object.

Reflexive Property A relation is *reflexive* if each element, **a**, bears that relation to itself.

Equality is a reflexive relation:

> For any number **a**, **a = a**.
> $$(12 = 12, \ 100 = 100, \ {}^{1}/_{2} = {}^{1}/_{2})$$

In words: Every number equals itself.

Note: Not every relation is reflexive: *less than* is not a reflexive relation: *12* is not less than *12*.

region A large, usually continuous, segment of a surface or space.

regular (figure) Having equal sides and equal angles.

relation Any ordered pair of numbers.

relationship A logical association between two or more objects.

relatively prime Two or more numbers that have no common factors other than **1**. The numbers themselves may or may not be prime, but they are said to be "prime, *relative to each other.*"

The GCF of relatively prime numbers is **1**.

remainder The number "left over" as a result when one integer is divided by another.

reverse Turned backward in position, direction, or order.

rhombus A quadrilateral with four equal sides and no right angles.

right angle An angle whose measure is 90°. Right angles are formed by the perpendicular intersection of two straight lines.

rotation In geometry, a transformation that turns a figure about a point.

rounding-off The process of expressing a number to the nearest specified place within a given number system (usually base 10).

Not exact; approximate. To express as a "round number."

row A series of objects placed next to each other, usually in a straight line.

rule A standard method or procedure for solving a class of problems.

WE'RE NUMBER 1
Fun Facts about 1:

- The number one represents "the whole thing."

- One is the only whole number that is neither prime nor composite.

- One has the special property that it is a FACTOR of every number: $N = 1 \cdot N$.

- Negative One is also a FACTOR of every number: $N = -1 \cdot -N$.

same Similar in kind, quality, quantity, or degree. See "THE LAW OF SAMEness."

sample A part of the total population. Used in statistics to generalize about the group.

scale Proper proportion.

scale factor The ratio of a distance measured on a scale drawing to the corresponding distance measured on the actual object.

scalene triangle A triangle with unequal sides and unequal angles.

scatter plot A graph of the points representing a collection of data.

scientific notation A shorthand way of writing very large or very small numbers.

A number in scientific notation is expressed as a decimal number between 1 and 10, multiplied by a power of 10.

score A group of 20 items.

section One of several parts; a piece.

sector The portion of a circle bounded by two radii and the included arc.

segment (of a line) A part of a line with a definite beginning and definite end.

sequence An ordered set of quantities.

series A number of objects arranged in a definable order.

set Any group of objects.

For a well-defined set, it is possible to determine whether or not a given object is a member of that set.

side A line bounding a plane figure. A surface bounding a solid figure.

sign A symbol (+ or –) that indicates whether a quantity is positive or negative.

similar Same shape, different size.

When two objects are similar, the corresponding angles are equal, and the corresponding line segments are proportional.

TRIANGLE

simultaneous equations Containing variables for which there are values that can satisfy all the equations at the same time.

sine A trigonometric function that is defined as the ratio of the leg opposite the angle to the hypotenuse of a right triangle.

single Consisting of one part.

skew lines Straight lines in space that are neither parallel nor intersecting.

skill Proficiency that is developed through training and experience.

skip counting Counting by equal intervals.

slide In geometry, a transformation where a figure moves in a given direction.

PRIME VS. COMPOSITE

A prime number is a number with exactly two distinct factors.

A composite number is a number with more than two distinct factors.

Using these definitions, one is neither prime nor composite because it has exactly one factor, namely, itself. Also, zero is the most composite number. Every number is a factor of 0, because every number goes into 0 exactly 0 times, with nothing left over.

Some numbers less than 100 appear to be prime because we do not encounter them when we learn our times tables. 39, 51, 57, 87, and 91 are such numbers. Note that the first four (39, 51, 57, and 87 all have 3 as a factor, and 91 has factors of 7 and 13).

3 x 13 = 39

S

ICOSAHEDRON

slope (of a line) A deviation from the horizontal. An inclined line.

Slope is also the amount that the dependent variable changes for each increase by one in the independent variable.

The slope of a line is defined as the "change in **y**" divided by the "change in **x**."

Socratic method (of teaching) Eliciting the desired response from students by a series of questions and answers designed to show the students that the answers are already contained in their minds. "Teaching by *asking* instead of *telling*."

solution The answer to a problem, especially an equation.

space The infinite extension of the 3-D field in which all matter exists.

speed The rate of change of the position of a moving body.

sphere The set of points in 3-D space, all of which are equidistant from a fixed point.

Compare with "circle."

square A quadrilateral with four equal sides and four equal (right) angles.

square root Two equal factors of a number (i.e., **4** is the square root of **16**).

square units The units used to measure area.

squared A number raised to the second power.

standard deviation A statistic that measures the dispersion of a sample data set.

steep Having a sharp inclination or slope.

stem-and-leaf A table utilizing digit(s) of a number as stems and the other plot digit(s) as leaves. For example, 5 | 7, 8 shows 57 and 58.

straight Extending continuously in the same direction without curving.

straight angle An angle whose measure is equal to 180°.

structure Something made up of a number of parts or objects that are held together by a set of rules.

substitution The act of replacing a quantity with an equal quantity.

subtraction Counting "how far apart two numbers are" and "how much is left." The process of removing a part(s) from a whole.

subtrahend The quantity that is subtracted from another quantity.

In $a - b = c$, b is the **subtrahend**.

In
$$\begin{array}{r} a \\ - b \\ \hline c \end{array}$$
b is the **subtrahend**.

sum The answer to an addition question.

surface The boundary of a 3-D figure. A portion of space having length and breadth but no thickness.

surface area The sum of the areas of all the faces, including the bases, of a 3-D object.

survey An interview, questionnaire, and/or a polling.

symmetric property A relation is *symmetric* if, for any two elements a and b, the positions of a and b can be switched and the relation remains true.

For all numbers a and b, if $a = b$, then $b = a$.

**If expression 1 = expression 2,
then expression 2 = expression 1.**

(If $2 + 3 = 4 + 1$, then $4 + 1 = 2 + 3$.)

[You can switch the quantities on the left and right sides of the equals sign.]

Note: Not all relations are symmetric. Greater Than is not a symmetric relation:

5 is greater than 2, but
2 is not greater than 5.

symmetry The property of "being exactly the same" on both sides of a dividing line or plane or about a center or an axis.

"SQUARE TREES HAVE SQUARE ROOTS."

- Larry Martinek

synthesis The combining of separate elements to form a coherent whole; the complex whole so formed.

Reasoning from the general to the particular; logical deduction.

system A group of interacting elements forming a complex whole.

take-away An informal word for the process of *subtraction*.

tangent A trigonometric function of an angle which is defined as the ratio of the lengths of the leg opposite to the leg adjacent to an angle in a right triangle.

Also, a line having one point in common with a curve.

term One of the quantities connected by addition or subtraction signs in an algebraic expression or equation. A part of a sum or difference in an algebraic expression.

A term consists of a group of numbers and variables multiplied together and is considered as a single entity.

$3ab$, $5xy^2$, 4^2, x, $4a^2bc^2$ are examples of *terms*.

tessellation A mosaic formed by repetitions of a single shape.

thing An individual object. An entity thought to have its own existence. A thought, a notion, or an utterance.

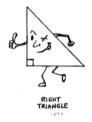

RIGHT
TRIANGLE

thirds A whole cut into three equal parts. One of the three equal parts.

time An interval separating two points on the continuum from yesterday, through today, and into tomorrow.

times Another word for the process of *multiplication*.

transformation The process of changing one quantity or object into another.

transitive property For all numbers **a**, **b**, and **c**, if **a** Δ **b** and **b** Δ **c**, then **a** Δ **c**.

A relation is *transitive* if it has the property that if **A** has the relationship (Δ) to **B**, and **B** has the same relationship to **C**, then **A** has the relationship (Δ) to **C**.

> Since **10 + 2 = 12** and **12 = 2 x 6**, then **10 + 2 = 2 x 6**.

> If **A** is in the same room as **B**, and **B** is in the same room as **C**, then **A** is in the same room as **C**.

Note: "Next to" is not a transitive relation. If A is next to B, and B is next to C, A is not necessarily next to C.

transversal A line that intersects a system of other lines, usually parallel lines.

trapezoid A quadrilateral with exactly one pair of parallel sides.

FRUSTRUM

triangle A three-sided, three-angled polygon. Three sides is the minimum number of sides that a polygon can have.

A *scalene triangle* has unequal sides and unequal angles.

An *isosceles triangle* has two equal sides and two equal angles.

An *equilateral triangle* has three equal sides and three equal angles.

An *acute triangle* has three acute angles.

A *right triangle* has one right angle.

An *obtuse triangle* has one obtuse angle.

trichotomy The property that, for any two given numbers **A** and **B**, one and only one of the following relationships is true:

Either $A = B$, $A > B$, or $A < B$.

In other words, either **A** is equal to **B**, or **A** is less than **B**, or **A** is greater than **B**. Only one of these can be true at a time.

trigonometry The study of three-angled figures (the study of triangles).

From the Latin: *tri* (three) + *gon* (angle) + *metry* (the measure of).

trinomial Consisting of or relating to three *names* or *terms*. A polynomial with three terms.

Compare with "binomial."

triple Composed of three like parts. Three times as many or as much.

twice Two times as many or as much. Double.

union The act of uniting into a new whole.

In Set Theory, the **union** of two or more sets is the set that contains all of the elements in all of the sets. Common elements are written only once in the set representing the union.

unit An individual, a group, a structure, or other entity regarded as an elementary structural or functional constituent of a whole.

unit fraction A fraction whose numerator is one.

unity One; the unit amount.

A fraction whose *value* is *one whole*.

universe All things, regarded as a whole.

unknown A quantity whose numerical value is not stated.

ZERO MEANS EVERYTHING

Fun Facts about 0:

- Zero is an EVEN number.

- Zero is the only number that is neither positive nor negative.

- Zero has the special property that any number times 0 equals 0: $0 \cdot N = 0$.

- Zero is the most composite number of all because every number divides INTO zero (every number goes in 0 times) with no remainder (nothing left over).

- No number can be divided BY 0. [Try to divide any number BY 0 on a calculator.]

validity An argument that is correctly inferred or deduced from a premise.

variable Something that changes; having no fixed quantitative value.

An unknown, used to represent a particular number.

A term used to help in understanding the study of algebraic structures, such as

$$a(b + c) = ab + ac.$$

NOTE: All variables are unknowns. In the expression "x + 3," the value of x is both variable and unknown.

On the other hand, not all unknowns are variables. In the equation "$\mathbf{x + 3 = 10}$," the value of $\mathbf{x}$ is unknown, but $\mathbf{x}$ is not variable. In this case, it is equal to 7, and only 7.

vector A quantity with both *magnitude* and *direction*.

vertex A meeting point of two lines that form an angle. The points where two line segments come together (corners). Also, a point where lines, rays, sides of a polygon or edges of a polyhedron meet (corner).

vertical At right angles to the horizon.

vinculum The horizontal bar in a fraction separating the numerator from the denominator. A grouping symbol.

void Completely lacking.

volume The amount of space inside a 3-D object, measured in cubic units.

weight A measure of the heaviness of an object.

whole Undivided. The one composed of the many. That which can be broken down into parts. *All* of the quantity under consideration.

Whole Number A member of the set {0, 1, 2, 3...}, (the *natural numbers* including 0).

width The measurement of the distance of something from side to side.

EQUILATERAL
TRIANGLE

Z

zero

zero The number that counts *none*. That which has no parts.

A point on the number line that divides the *positive* numbers from the *negative* numbers.

The power index that transforms any quantity into unity.

zero angle An angle whose measure equals 0°.

zillion An unspecified, very large, finite number.

WHOLE NUMBERS

A whole number is a number without a fractional part—no common or decimal fraction.

Examples: 1, 12, 667, 999

Notice that whole numbers come from counting by 1s.

CYLINDER

UNITY

A fraction whose value is equal to one whole (**1**).

Examples: $^2/_2$, $^4/_4$, $^9/_9$, 1

Notice that the numerator (the top number) is equal to the denominator (the bottom number).

IMPROPER FRACTION

A fraction whose value is greater than one whole (**1**).

Examples: $^3/_2$, $^9/_4$, $^{23}/_{12}$, $^{17}/_9$

Notice that the numerator (the top number) is greater than the denominator (the bottom number).

FRACTIONS

A fraction is a part of a whole. The denomination (the name) of a fraction is the number of equal parts in the whole.

Example: If a whole is broken into four equal parts, the denomination (the name) of the fraction is fourths. If we count three of these parts, then we have created the fraction three-fourths ($^3/4$).

PROPER FRACTION

A fraction whose value is less than one whole (**1**).

Examples: $^1/2$, $^5/9$, $^3/4$, $^{19}/20$

Notice that the numerator (the top number) is less than the denominator (the bottom number).

MIXED NUMBER

A number that is a mixture of a whole number and a fraction.

A mixed number is another name for an improper fraction.

Examples: $3^1/2$, $2^3/4$, $5^7/9$, $1^3/11$

Notice that the value of a mixed number is always greater than **1**.

50

HALF — "2 PARTS THE SAME"

Half is the primal fraction, the first occurrence of a whole being broken-down into equal parts; in this case, "two parts the same." It is the easiest fraction to demonstrate, and is, therefore, the easiest to understand.

The way in which half behaves when added, subtracted, multiplied, and divided serves as a model for the actions of all the other fractions.

By learning all about half first, the study of the other fractions becomes an extension of known ideas.

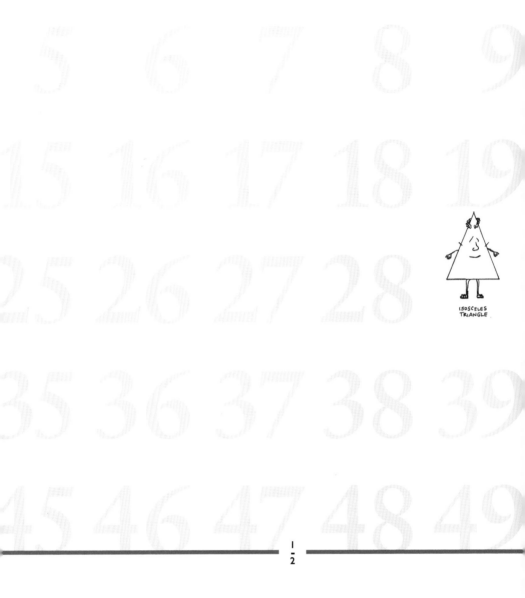

ISOSCELES
TRIANGLE

$$\frac{1}{2}$$

Appendix 1 : Special Word Sets

Ordinal Numbers are numbers that indicate *position* in ranked order.

first
second
third
...etc.

Prefixes—Combining forms that modify the main word.

poly- many
mono- / uni- one (1)
bi- two (2)
tri- three (3)
quad- four (4)
quin- / pent- five (5)
hex- / sex- six (6)
hept- / sept- seven (7)
oct- eight (8)
non- nine (9)
dec- ten (10)

cent- hundred (100)
mil- thousand (1,000)

mega- 1,000 thousands (1,000,000)
giga- 1,000 megas (1,000,000,000)
tetra- 1,000 gigas (1,000,000,000,000)

milli- thousandth (1/1,000 = 0.001)
micro- millionth (1/1,000,000 = 0.000001)
nano- billionth (1/1,000,000,000 = 0.000000001)

circ- around
dia- across
peri- around

Stems

-gon angle
-lateral side
-meter measure

Names for large numbers

thousand	A thousand ones (1s).
million	A thousand thousands (one set of a thousand 1,000s).
billion	A thousand thousand thousands (two sets of a thousand 1,000s).
trillion	A thousand thousand thousand thousands (three sets of a thousand 1,000s).
quadrillion	Four sets of a thousand 1,000s.
quintillion	Five sets of a thousand 1,000s.
sextillion	Six sets of a thousand 1,000s.
septillion	Seven sets of a thousand 1,000s.
octillion	Eight sets of a thousand 1,000s.
nonillion	Nine sets of a thousand 1,000s.
decillion	Ten sets of a thousand 1,000s.
zillion	Not a number. It is an expression meaning an unspecified large quantity.

Names for polygons

triangle	A (3) three-sided polygon.
quadrilateral	A (4) four-sided polygon.
pentagon	A (5) five-sided polygon.
hexagon	A (6) six-sided polygon.
heptagon	(**septagon**) A (7) seven-sided polygon.
octagon	An (8) eight-sided polygon.
nonagon	A (9) nine-sided polygon.
decagon	A (10) ten-sided polygon.

TEACHER SAYS
There is a need for a "sense check"
at each step in the learning process.
Otherwise:

Teacher says: "Two cans are worth 25 cents."

55

Appendix 2 : A Close-up on
"Math" Related Words

RECTANGULAR
SOLID (BOX)

Let's build the word "mathematics" from parts:

ma the basic ma represents the most fundamental of all sounds, the cry or murmur of a babe for the breast.

Mother Nature.

In the classic distinction between "Spirit" and "Form," **ma** is Form.

ma is the root of many words that involve existence and learning.

mat anything closely interwoven; composed of strands.

mata thought (Sanskrit).

matter the "stuff" of existence
        (material, mass, manifestation).

matrix that which gives origin, form, or foundation to something enclosed or embedded in it, the womb. A framework.

mathesis the activity of learning; science, learning: mental discipline.

matheia body of learning.

mathetic of or having to do with learning.

mathematicus disposed to learn, belonging to learning or the sciences (L).

mathema that which is learnt.

L = Latin Root

G = Greek Root

math to learn (a Greek stem).

thema the subject at hand (G).

-atics of or pertaining to; possesses the nature of (as in system*atic*, "is like a system"); a suffix used in forming the names of sciences, as acoust*ics*, dynam*ics*, statist*ics*, polit*ics*, and athlet*ics*.

ma-them-atics the science of **learning**.

The limited sense of the word **mathematics**, referring to number and symbol manipulation, developed because in the early days learning was primarily concerned with surveying, astrology, astronomy, and the calculation of the calendar, all things that naturally involve numbers.

RELATED WORDS...

mathetic pertaining to learning or scientific knowledge.

polymath a person extremely and diversely erudite; learned in many subjects.

opsimath one who begins to learn late in life; a "late bloomer."

philomath a lover of learning.

chrestomathy literally "useful learning."

ARITHMETIC

From the Latin *arithmetica*, "the art of counting"—the Greek *arithmos* — "number."

ars metrica, "the art of measure."

From the Indo-European bases *ar-* "to join" and *ri–* "to count, number" + *–metiri* "to measure."

ALGEBRA

Algebra redintegration or reunion of broken parts, literally: the reduction.

From Arabic *al* (the) + *jabara* (to reunite),

from *jabara*: to bind together, to reunite, redintegrate, consolidate, restore; the surgical treatment of fractures, bonesetting,

from Arabic *al jabara*:

- reduction of parts to whole,
- reunion of broken parts,
- setting of bones.

Algebra The department of Mathematics which investigates the relations and properties of numbers by means of general symbols; and, in a more abstract sense, a calculus of symbols combined according to certain defined laws (rules).

The science of redintegration and equation (opposition, comparison, collation).

GEOMETRY

literally, "measurement of the earth,"

geo- a combining form meaning "earth," and

-metery a combining form meaning "the process of measuring."

RECTANGLE

TRIGONOMETRY

trigon- a combining form meaning "triangular" and

-metry a combining form meaning "the process of measuring."

CALCULUS

A method of calculation. A small stone, pebble, stone in the kidneys or bladder; a stone used in reckoning.

The Calculus, as developed by Leibniz and Newton, is *the mathematics of* **change**.

IMPORTANT WORD ROOTS IN MATHEMATICS

CUBE

Knowledge of a handful of key word roots is a big help in learning mathematics vocabulary. Knowledge of these roots makes many technical words "self-decoding." Here are some of the more important ones.

1) *dia-* "through, across"
   diagnosis - "knowing through and through"
   diagonal - "through an angle; across from angle to angle"
   diameter - "the measure across (through) a circle"

2) *circ-* "around"
   circus - "theater in the round"
   circuit - "a complete path around"
   circulate - "move around"
   circle - "a round figure"
   circumference - "the distance around a circle"

3) *gon-* "angle"
   polygon - "a figure with many angles"
   diagonal - "through an angle"

4) *mono-* "one"
   monorail - "a train that runs on a single rail"
   monomial - "an expression with one term"

5) *bi-* "two"
   bicycle- "two wheels"
   binocular - "two eyes"
   binomial - "an expression with two terms"
   bisect - "cut into two (equal) pieces"

6) *tri-* "three"
   tricycle - "three wheels"
   triangle - "a figure with exactly three angles"
   trinomial - "an expression with three terms"

7) *qua-* "four"
   quart - "one-fourth of a gallon"
   quarter - "one-fourth part of a whole"
   quadrilateral - "a figure with exactly four sides"

8) *poly-* "many"
polylingual - "speaks many languages"
polymath - "one who has knowledge of many subjects"
polygon - "a figure with many angles"
polynomial - "an expression with many terms"

9) *ra-* "a projection from a source"
radio - "to project through (dia- Greek, 'through')"
radius - "a projection from the center to the edge of a circle"
ray - "an infinite projection from a point"

10) *me-* "measure"
medicus - "a measure of man's ills and injuries"
meditation - "thought—measuring an idea, a fact, thing"
mete- "to measure out (as in punishment)"
metric - "measurement"
meter - "a device for measuring"
meter - "a unit of distance in the metric system"
mean - "the measure of the middle–the average"

11) *se-* "to follow," "to cut; separate"
second - "following the first"
series - "a number of similar things arranged one thing after another"
sequence - "one thing after another"
segregate - "to set apart from others"
section - "a cutting apart, a part cut off"
sector - "a part of"
segment - "any of the parts into which something is separated"
secant - "a line that cuts a curve"

12) *peri-* "around"
periscope - "a device for looking around"
period - literally "way around"
perihelion- "around the sun"
perimeter - "the measure (distance) around a figure"

thing From the Indo-European root tenkos-, from the base ten- "to extend (in space and time)"..."meeting at a fixed time"..."assembly."

Whatever exists, or is conceived to exist, as a separate entity or as a distinct and individual quality, fact, or idea.

An abstract quality or entity; that which is or may become an object of thought, whether material or ideal, animate or inanimate, actual, possible, or imaginary.

Being, individual. A separatable or distinguishable object of thought:

- a thought, idea, word, statement, or thesis
- a matter of concern, a point of contention, an issue
- a task or job
- a particular state of affairs
- an aim, objective
- a deed, act, accomplishment
- an idea, notion
- a detail, quality, point, particular
- an event, circumstance
- the product of work or activity
- an artistic composition
- a possession
- a living being or creature
- an inanimate object as distinguished from a living being.

The real or actual essence or substance as distinguished from its appearance or from a name, word, or symbol for it.

An entity that can be thought of or is known as having existence in space and time as distinguished from that which is purely an object of thought.

RHOMBUS

- An object or entity that cannot or need not be precisely designated.
- Something special or unique that one feels disposed to; what one wants to do.
- The proper, right, desirable, required, or fashionable way of behaving, talking, dressing ...used with the word "the," for example, "the thing you are talking about."
- A mild obsession or phobia; an irrational liking, fear, etc.

thingy Real; material.

thing-in-itself An ultimate reality unqualified by the subjective mood of human perception and thought; a metaphysical reality.

"a thing or two" Something worth knowing or telling; something proving equality or superiority of knowledge.

Any or all of the characters presented in this book. Thank you, things.

64

NUMBER SIXTY-FOUR (64)
64 is both a PERFECT SQUARE (8 x 8)
and a PERFECT CUBE (4 x 4 x 4).

Appendix 3 : Number Systems

Natural Numbers (*N*) Also called *Counting Numbers,* Natural Numbers are the positive numbers that do not contain fractions.

$$N = \{1, 2, 3...\}$$

Whole Numbers (*W*) The *Whole Numbers* are 0 and the positive numbers that do not contain fractions (the Counting Numbers and 0).

$$W = \{0, 1, 2, 3...\}$$

Integers (*Z*) The *Integers* are the positive and negative *Whole Numbers,* including 0 (the *Whole Numbers* and their opposites).

$$Z = \{...-3, -2, -1, 0, 1, 2, 3...\}$$

Rational Numbers (*Q*) The *Rational Numbers* have the form $^a/_b$, where **a** and **b** are *integers* and $b \neq 0$. That is, they are all the numbers that can be written as *a ratio (a fraction)*.

All the *Rational Numbers* can be written as common fractions, as decimal fractions, and as percents.

The decimal form of a *Rational Number* is either a *repeating* decimal or a *terminating* decimal.

Examples: $1/4 = 0.25 = 25\%$
$1/3 = 0.333... = 33^1/_3\%$

Irrational Numbers (*I*) The *Irrational Numbers* are numbers that cannot be written as fractions. Their decimal representations do not repeat and do not terminate.

> **Examples:**
> $$\pi = 3.14159...$$
> $$\sqrt{2} = 1.414213...$$
> $$x = 0.010010001...$$

PARALLELOGRAM

Real Numbers (*R*) *The Real Numbers* are all of the *Rational* and *Irrational Numbers* taken together.

> **Examples:** All of the above.

Complex Numbers (*C*) The *Complex Numbers* are all the *Real Numbers* and numbers that involve the square root of negative one ($\sqrt{-1}$). *Complex Numbers* have the general form **a** + **b***i*, where **a** and **b** are *real* numbers and $i = \sqrt{-1}$. **a** is the *real* part and **b***i* is called the *imaginary* part. (For *Real Numbers*, **b** = 0. For **PURE** *Imaginary* numbers, **a** = 0.)

> **Examples:** All of the above (where **b** = 0), and 3 + 2i, 5 - 6i (where **b** ≠ 0).

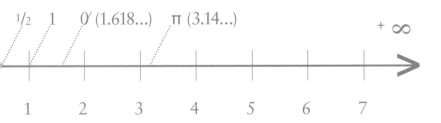

TETRAHEDRON
(PYRAMID)

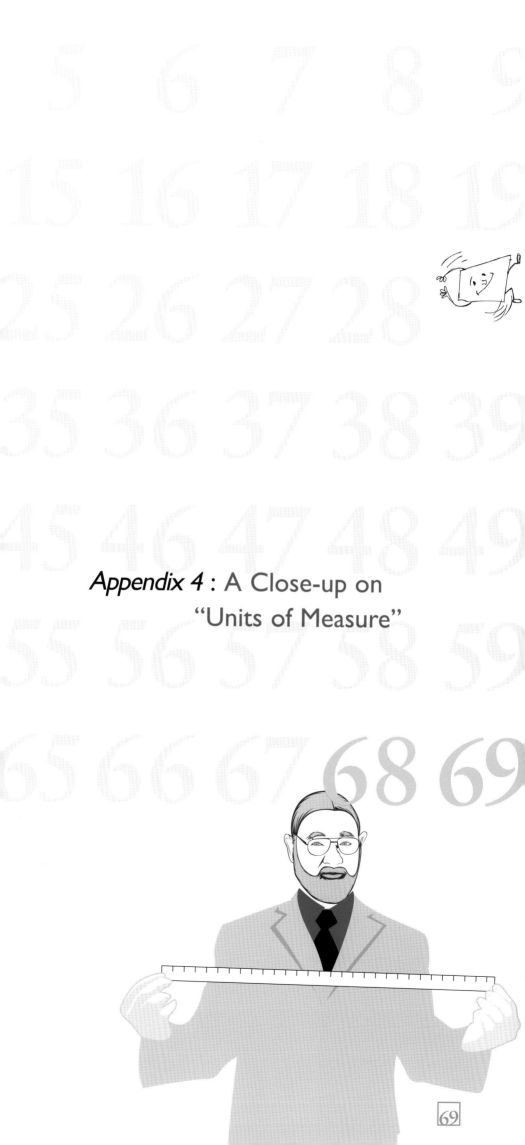

Appendix 4 : A Close-up on "Units of Measure"

1 foot	12 inches
1 yard	3 feet = 36 inches
1 mile	5,280 feet = 1,760 yards
1 minute	60 seconds
1 hour	60 minutes
1 day	24 hours
1 week	7 days
1 fortnight	2 weeks = 14 days
1 year	365 days (regular year) 366 days (leap year)
1 year	12 months
1 year	52 weeks and 1 day (2 days in leap years)
1 score	20 years = 2 decades
1 decade	10 years = $1/2$ score
1 century	100 years = 10 decades
1 millennium	1,000 years = 100 decades = 10 centuries
1 pound	16 ounces
1 ton	2,000 pounds
1 gallon	4 quarts
1 quart	2 pints
1 pint	2 cups
1 cup	8 fluid ounces
1 fathom	6 feet / 2 yards
1 league	3 miles
1 furlong	$1/8$ of-a-mile
speed of light	186,000 miles per second (approx.)
1 light-year	6,000,000,000,000 miles (approx.)
1 parsec	3.3 light-years (approx.)

1 inch equals exactly **2.54** centimeters.

1 kilometer is a little more than **1** half of a mile.

1 liter is a little more than **1** quart.

1 kilogram = **1,000** grams = about **2.2** pounds.

QUADRILATERAL

SHORT UNITS OF LENGTH

1 micrometer = 0.001 millimeter

1 nanometer (nm) = 0.001 micrometer

1 angstrom (Å) = 0.0000001 millimeter

LONG UNITS OF LENGTH

1 U.S. statute mile (mi) = 5,280 feet

1 astronomical unit = 93,000,000 (93 million) miles
(the average distance from the Earth to the Sun)

UNITS OF DRY VOLUME & WEIGHT

1 ounce (oz)	16 drams 437 1/2 grains
1 pound (lb)	16 ounces 256 drams 7,000 grains
1 bushel (bu)	4 pecks = 2,150.42 cubic inches = 32 quarts
1 pint	4 gills
1 quart	2 pints
1 gallon	4 quarts
1 peck	2 gallons
1 bushel	8 gallons (4 pecks)
1 quarter	8 bushels

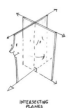

INTERSECTING
PLANES

APOTHECARY UNITS OF MASS

1 scruple	20 grains (exactly)
1 dram	60 grains (exactly) = 3 scruples
1 ounce apothecaries (oz ap)	8 drams apothecaries 24 scruples = 480 grains
1 pound apothecaries (lb ap)	12 ounces apothecaries 96 drams apothecaries 288 scruples = 5,760 grains

[The "grain" is the same in avoirdupois, troy, and apothecaries units of mass.]

TROY UNITS OF MASS

1 pennyweight (dwt)	24 grains
1 ounce troy (oz t)	20 pennyweights = 480 grains
1 pound troy (lb t)	12 ounces troy 240 pennyweights = 5,760 grains

[The "grain" is the same in avoirdupois, troy, and apothecaries units of mass.]

RARELY USED UNITS OF LENGTH

1 link (li)	8 inches = 0.66 feet
1 rod (rd), pole, or perch	16 1/2 feet
1 chain (ch)	100 links = 4 rods = 66 feet
1 cable's length	120 fathoms 720 feet 219 meters
1 U.S. statute	80 chains = 320 rods = 1 mile = 5,280 feet

MISC. UNITS OF MEASURE

1 carat (c)	200 milligrams (exactly) 3.086 grains
1 Point (typography)	$1/72$ inch (approximately) 0.351 millimeter
1 acre	43,560 square feet
1 hectare	2.471 acres
1 hand	4 inches
1 barrel (bbl), liquid	31 to 42 gallons

There are a variety of "barrels" established by law or usage.

For example:

- Federal taxes on fermented liquors are based on a barrel of 31 gallons,
- Many State laws fix the "barrel for liquids" as 31 $1/2$ gallons,
- Federal law recognizes a 40-gallon barrel for "proof spirits," and
- 42 gallons comprise a barrel of crude oil or petroleum products for statistical purposes.

1 tablespoon	3 teaspoons / 15 milliliters / 4 fluid drams / $1/2$ fluid ounce
1 teaspoon	5 milliliters

10^{24}	**yotta**	(Y)	*octo*, "eight" (L and G)
10^{21}	**zetta**	(Z)	*septem*, "seven"(L)
10^{18}	**exa**	(E)	*hex*, "six" (G)
10^{15}	**peta**	(P)	*pente*, "five" (G)
10^{12}	**tera**	(T)	*teras*, "monster" (G)
10^{9}	**giga**	(G)	*gigas*, "giant" (G)
10^{6}	**mega**	(M)	*megas*, "large" (G)
10^{3}	**kilo**	(k)	*chilioi*, "thousand" (G)
10^{2}	**hecto**	(h)	*hekaton*, "hundred" (G)
10^{1}	**deka**	(de)	*deka*, "ten" (G)
10^{-1}	**deci**	(d)	*decimus*, "tenth"(L)
10^{-2}	**centi**	(c)	*centum*, "hundredth" (L)
10^{-3}	**milli**	(m)	*mille*, "thousandth" (L)
10^{-6}	**micro**	(mu)	*micro* (L) or *mikros*, (G) "small"
10^{-9}	**nano**	(n)	*nanus* (L) or *nanos*, (G) "dwarf"
10^{-12}	**pico**	(p)	*pico*, "a bit" (Sp) or *piccolo*, "small" (Itn)
10^{-15}	**femto**	(f)	*femten*, "fifteen" (Danish-Norwegian)
10^{-18}	**atto**	(a)	*atten*, "eighteen" (Danish-Norwegian)
10^{-21}	**zepto**	(z)	*septem*, "seven" (L)
10^{-24}	**yocto**	(y)	*octo*, "eight" (L and G)

L = Latin Root

G = Greek Root

2 DOCTORS = 1 PARADOX

1,024 MICROPHONES = 1 megaphone

KITE

THE SHORTEST DISTANCE BETWEEN TWO JOKES = A STRAIGHT LINE

10 AIDES = 1 DECADE

WHAT'S A LIGHT YEAR? THE SAME AS A REGULAR YEAR, ONLY LESS CALORIES.

HOW DO YOU MAKE 7 EVEN? TAKE AWAY THE "S."

THE LAW OF SAMEness

When adding or subtracting, you can only numerically combine things that have the same name.

Examples:

> 2 apples + 3 apples = 5 apples
> 2 sevenths + 3 sevenths = 5 sevenths
> $2x + 3x = 5x$

whereas,

> 2 apples + 3 bananas ≠ 5 banapples
> 2 thirds + 3 fourths ≠ 5 sevenths
> $2x + 3y \neq 5xy$

Appendix 5 : Properties of Real Numbers
& The Laws of Mathematics

THE RULE OF THE WHOLE

The whole is equal to the sum of its parts.

In symbols:

$$W = P_1 + P_2 + P_3 + \ldots + P_i + \ldots + P_n$$

Example:

> A piggy bank contains 3 pennies, 4 nickels, and 5 dimes.
>
> The total number of coins (the *whole*) equals the number of pennies, plus the number of nickels, plus the number of dimes (the *parts*).
>
> total number of coins = 3 + 4 + 5 = 12

THE RULE OF THE PARTS

Each part equals the whole *minus* the *sum* of all the other **parts**.

In symbols:

$$P_i = W - (P_1 + P_2 + \ldots + P_{i-1} + P_{i+1} + \ldots + P_n)$$

Example:

> A piggy bank contains 25 coins.
>
> Five of the coins are pennies, 6 are nickels, 4 are dimes, and the rest are quarters.
>
> The number of quarters (one of the parts) equals the total number of coins (the whole) minus the combined total of pennies, nickels, and dimes (the other parts).
>
> number of quarters = 25 − (5 + 6 + 4) = 10

THE CANCELLATION LAW

Note: all variables may be as *simple* or as *complex* as you please.

Equal quantities on both sides of the equals sign can be cancelled.

TRAPEZOID

In symbols:

If $x + a = y + a$, then $x = y$.
If $x - a = y - a$, then $x = y$.
If $ax = ay$, then $x = y$
  [where $a \neq 0$].

If $x/a = y/a$, then $x = y$
  [where $a \neq 0$].

— the a *cancels* from both sides —

If $(a + b)x = (a + b)y$, then $x = y$

— the $(a + b)$ *cancels* from both sides —

Example:

If $x + 3 = 7 + 3$, then $x = 7$.
If $x - 5 = 15 - 5$, then $x = 15$.
If $3x = 3 \cdot 9$, then $x = 9$.
If $x/3 = 15/3$, then $x = 15$.

If $(3 + 4)x = (3 + 4) \cdot 5$, then $x = 5$.

PSYCHOLOGY OF MATH

Notice that the second term in each pair is a negative psychology term.

even—odd	real—imaginary
positive—negative	power—radical
rational—irrational	proper—improper

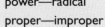

THE SUBSTITUTION LAW

PLANE

Equals may be substituted for equals.

In symbols:

If $a = b$, then b can replace any occurrence of a.

If $a = b$ and $b + c = d$, then $a + c = d$
(b is replaced by a in the second equation).

If $a = b$ and $bc = d$, then $ac = d$
(b is replaced by a in the second equation).

Examples:

If $b = 3$ and $a + b = 7$, then $a + 3 = 7$.
If $a = 5$ and $ab = 12$, then $5b = 12$.

"Things equal to the same thing are equal to each other."

In symbols:

If $a = b$ and $c = b$, then $a = c$
(a and c are both equal to b; so $a = c$).

Examples:

If $a = 3$ and $b + c = 3$, then $a = b + c$.
If $a = b$ and $cx = b$, then $a = cx$.

THE CLOSURE PROPERTY

THE CLOSURE PROPERTY OF ADDITION

For all real numbers a and b, a + b is a real number. Thus, the Real Numbers are closed under addition. (When you add two real numbers, you get another real number.)

Also, the sum is *unique*. (There is one and only one answer for a given pair of numbers.)

Examples:

$$10 + 2 = 12$$
$$1/2 + 1/3 = 5/6$$

THE CLOSURE PROPERTY OF MULTIPLICATION

For all real numbers a and b, a • b is a real number. Thus, the Real Numbers are closed under all of the operations (addition, subtraction, multiplication, and division). (When you operate on two real numbers, you get another real number.)

Also, the answer is *unique*. (There is one and only one answer for a given pair of numbers and a given operation.)

Examples:

$$-2 • 6 = -12$$
$$0.2 • 0.3 = 0.06$$

Note: The Positive Numbers are not closed under subtraction: 2 − 7 is not a positive number. The Whole Numbers are not closed under division: 7 ÷ 2 is not a whole number.

THE DISTRIBUTIVE PROPERTY OF MULTIPLICATION OVER ADDITION & SUBTRACTION

For any numbers a, b, and c,

$$a \cdot (b + c) = a \cdot b + a \cdot c$$
$$a \cdot (b - c) = a \cdot b - a \cdot c$$

In words:

> The product of the sum equals the sum of the products. The product of the difference equals the difference of the products. You get the same answer if you operate on the whole, "a times the quantity (b + c)," or on the parts "the sum of a times b and a times c separately."

Examples:

$$2 \cdot (4 + 3) = 2 \cdot 4 + 2 \cdot 3$$
$$2 \cdot (2x - 3y) = 4x - 6y$$

THE UnDISTRIBUTIVE PROPERTY OF MULTIPLICATION OVER ADDITION AND SUBTRACTION

For any numbers a, b, and c,

$$a \cdot b + a \cdot c = a \cdot (b + c)$$
$$a \cdot b - a \cdot c = a \cdot (b - c)$$

In words:

> The sum of the products equals the product of the sum. The difference of the products equals the product of the difference. UnDistributing is the process of "pulling out" a common factor from the sum of two or more terms. This process is also called "factoring."

Examples:

$$8 + 6 = 2 \cdot 4 + 2 \cdot 3 = 2 \cdot (4 + 3)$$
$$6x + 8y - 10z = 2(3x + 4y - 5z)$$

THE DISTRIBUTIVE PROPERTY OF DIVISION OVER ADDITION

PENTAGON

For any numbers a, b, and c,

$$(b + c) \div a = (b \div a) + (c \div a)$$

In words:

> The quotient of the sum equals the sum of the quotients. You get the same answer if you operate on the whole "the quantity (b + c) divided by a," or on the parts, "the sum of 'b divided by a' and 'c divided by a' separately."

Example:

$$(15 + 12) \div 3 = 15 \div 3 + 12 \div 3$$

THE DISTRIBUTIVE PROPERTY OF DIVISION OVER SUBTRACTION

For any numbers a, b, and c,

$$(b - c) \div a = (b \div a) - (c \div a)$$

In words:

> The quotient of the difference equals the difference of the quotients. You get the same answer if you operate on the whole, "the quantity (b − c) divided by a," or on the parts, "the difference of 'b divided by a' and 'c divided by a' separately."

Example:

$$(15 - 12) \div 3 = 15 \div 3 - 12 \div 3$$

ELLIPSE

DISTRIBUTING A MINUS SIGN IN FRONT OF PARENTHESIS

For any numbers a, b, and c,

$$-(a + b - c) = -a - b + c$$

In words:

> A minus sign outside of parenthesis distributes a -1 to each of the terms in the parenthesis. Another way to say this is: "a minus sign outside of parenthesis changes all the signs inside the parenthesis, and leaves the rest of the terms unchanged."

Examples:

$$-(2x - 3b + 4c) = -2x + 3b - 4c$$
$$-(-3x + 2y - 7) = 3x - 2y + 7$$

$$70 < 71 < 72$$

LITTLE-KNOWN FACT

The arrowheads on the Number Line are the "greater than" sign (>) [numbers get bigger to the right], and the "less than" sign (<) [numbers get smaller to the left].

THE COMMUTATIVE PROPERTY OF ADDITION

For all numbers a and b,

$$a + b = b + a$$

In words:

It doesn't matter in which order you add two numbers.

Example:

$$9 + 3 = 3 + 9$$

THE COMMUTATIVE PROPERTY OF MULTIPLICATION

For all numbers a and b,

$$a \cdot b = b \cdot a$$

In words:

It doesn't matter in which order you multiply two numbers.

Example:

$$9 \cdot 3 = 3 \cdot 9$$

Notes: Subtraction is not commutative: $9 - 3 \neq 3 - 9$
Division is not commutative: $9 \div 3 \neq 3 \div 9$.

THE ASSOCIATIVE PROPERTY OF ADDITION

For all numbers a, b, and c,

$$(a + b) + c = a + (b + c)$$

In words:

It doesn't matter in what order you group numbers when adding.

Example:

$$(2 + 3) + 4 = 2 + (3 + 4)$$

THE ASSOCIATIVE PROPERTY OF MULTIPLICATION

For all numbers a, b, and c,

$$(a \cdot b) \cdot c = a \cdot (b \cdot c)$$

In words:

It doesn't matter in what order you group numbers when multiplying.

Example:

$$(2 \cdot 3) \cdot 4 = 2 \cdot (3 \cdot 4)$$

Notes: Subtraction is not associative: $(9 - 6) - 3 \neq 9 - (6 - 3)$
Division is not associative: $(9 \div 6) \div 3 \neq 9 \div (6 \div 3)$.

THE IDENTITY PROPERTY OF (0)

THE ADDITION PROPERTY OF ZERO

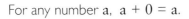

(The Identity Element for Addition)

HEXAGON

Zero is the Identity Element for addition because, when it is added to a number, it leaves the number unchanged; it preserves the number's identity.

For any number a, $a + 0 = a$.

In words:

Any number plus zero equals itself.

Example:

$12 + 0 = 12$

THE SUBTRACTION PROPERTY OF ZERO

(The Identity Element for Subtraction)

Zero is the Identity Element for subtraction because, when it is subtracted from a number, it leaves the number unchanged; it preserves the number's identity.

For any number a, $a - 0 = a$

In words:

Any number minus zero equals itself.

Example:

$12 - 0 = 12$

$3 \times 29 = 87$

CIRCLE

THE MULTIPLICATION PROPERTY OF ONE

(The Identity Element for Multiplication)

One is the Identity Element for multiplication because, when it multiplies another number, it leaves the number unchanged; it preserves the number's identity.

For any number a, $a \cdot 1 = a$

In words:

Any number times one equals itself.

Example:

$12 \cdot 1 = 12$

THE DIVISION PROPERTY OF ONE

(The Identity Element for Division)

One is the Identity Element for division because, when it divides another number, it leaves the number unchanged; it preserves the number's identity.

For any number $a, a \div 1 = a$

In words:

Any number divided by one equals itself.

Example:

$12 \div 1 = 12$

THE INVERSE PROPERTY OF ADDITION

For each number, a, there exists a number -a
such that $a + -a = 0$

In words:

> Every number has an opposite, and
> the number plus its opposite equals the
> Identity Element for addition.

Examples:

> $12 + -12 = 0,$
> $-3^1/4 + 3^1/4 = 0$

INVERSE PROPERTY OF MULTIPLICATION

For each number, a, $(a \neq 0)$, there exists a
number $1/a$ such that $(a)(1/a) = 1$

In words:

> Every number has a reciprocal, and the
> number times its reciprocal equals the
> Identity Element for multiplication.

Examples:

> $(4)(^1/4) = 1$
> $(^2/5)(^5/2) = 1$

THE MULTIPLICATION PROPERTY OF ZERO

For any number a, a • 0 = 0

In words:

Any number times zero is zero.

Example:

12 • 0 = 0

THE DIVISION PROPERTY OF ZERO

For any number a, 0 ÷ a = 0

In words:

Zero divided by any number is zero.

Example:

0 ÷ 12 = 0

Note: Division *by* zero does not yield a unique answer. Thus, we say it is undefined.

> " MATHEMATICS NEED NOT BE A MYSTERY. WHEN PROPERLY TAUGHT, MATH IS AN ADVENTURE, NOT A VEHICLE FOR 'DUTIFUL SUFFERING.' "
>
> - Larry Martinek

7 x 13 = 91

THE SUBTRACTION PROPERTY OF ALL NUMBERS

For any number a, $a - a = 0$

In words:

Any number minus itself is zero.

Example:

$12 - 12 = 0$

HEPTAGON
(SEPTAGON)

THE DIVISION PROPERTY OF ALL NUMBERS

(except 0)

For any number a, $a \div a = 1$

In words:

Any number divided by itself is **1**.

Example:

$12 \div 12 = 1$

DECAGON

A relation is reflexive if each element, **a**, bears that relation to itself.

Example:

For any number a, a = a (12 = 12).

In words:

Every number equals *itself.*

Note: *Less Than* is not a reflexive relation: 12 is not less than 12.

3. Find x.

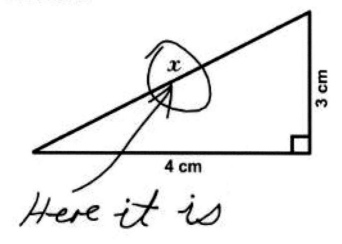

Here it is

A relation is symmetric if, for any two elements a and b, the positions of a and b can be switched and the relation remains true.

Example:

For all numbers a and b, If a = b, then b = a.
(If 2 + 3 = 5, then 5 = 2 + 3.)

In words:

If **expression** 1 = **expression** 2, then
expression 2 = **expression** 1.

You can switch the quantities on the left and right sides of the equals sign.

Note: *Greater Than* is not a symmetric relation: 5 is greater than 2, but 2 is not greater than 5.

" 'SHOW ALL YOUR WORK' SHOULD BE COMPLEMENTED WITH, 'EXPLAIN ALL OF YOUR THINKING.' "

- Larry Martinek

For all numbers **a**, **b**, and **c**,
if **a** = **b** and **b** = **c**, then **a** = **c**.

In words:

A relation is transitive if it has the property
that, if a has a relationship to b, and b has
the same relationship to c, then a has the
same relationship to c.

Examples:

Since 10 + 2 = 12 and 12 = 2 x 6,
then 10 + 2 = 2 x 6.

If a is in the same room as b, and b is in the
same room as c, then a is in the same room as c.

Note: Next to is not a transitive relation: if a is next to b,
and b is next to c, a is not necessarily next to c.

LITTLE-KNOWN FACT
The percent sign (%) is the digits in the number
100 rewritten 010, with 1 at a slant (%).

OPERATORS, OPERANDS, & OPERATIONS

operand Δ operator = result

Δ is a given binary operation
   (addition, subtraction, multiplication, division)

OCTAGON

ADDITION

operand + operator = result

   $8 + 9 = 17$

[8 (the operand) is operated on by 9 (the operator), using addition (the operation), resulting in 17.]

SUBTRACTION

operand - operator = result

   $13 - 8 = 5$

[13 (the operand) is operated on by 8 (the operator), using subtraction (the operation), resulting in 5.]

MULTIPLICATION

operand x operator = result

   $3 \times 4 = 12$

[3 (the operand) is operated on by 4 (the operator), using multiplication (the operation), resulting in 12.]

DIVISION

operand ÷ operator = result

   $42 \div 7 = 6$

[42 (the operand) is operated on by 7 (the operator), using division (the operation), resulting in 6.]

ON DENOMINATION, QUANTITY, & VALUE

ENNEAGON
(NONAGON)

"How many, of what, worth how much?"

There are several key concepts that unify the mathematics curriculum and are critical elements in one's ability to be a good problem solver.

DENOMINATION ("THE NAME OF")

Every ***thing*** has a name. This name gives the denomination of the thing, making it unique within a larger group of things.

"Tuna, shark, and salmon are denominations of fish."

"Halves, quarters, and thirds are denominations of fractions."

"Pennies, nickels, dimes, and quarters are denominations of coins."

QUANTITY ("THE NUMBER OF")

After knowing the name of some ***thing***, you should also know the quantity of that thing in the given problem.

"3 nickels"   **quantity** = 3

"half-of-a-dozen"   **quantity** = $1/2$ and 6

"2 hours in minutes"   **quantity** = 120

Value ("how much each one is worth")

Many quantities have a value associated with them.

"Cost per pound"   "$3.69 per pound."

"Worth of each"   "Dimes are worth
                        10 cents each."

"Units of Measure"   "One mile equals
                        5,280 feet."

Relating Denomination, Quantity, and Value

Many problems can be solved using the idea that:

Total   =   [quantity times value] of the first
            thing + [quantity times value] of
            the second thing + ... [quantity
            times value] of the last thing.

When more than one thing is involved, The Law
of SAMEness comes into play.

[See "**The Law of SAMEness.**"]

Math
= knowledge (Latin)

here we go!

nas-
= birth (Latin)

-ium
= place of (Latin)

Mathnasium
= the birthplace of knowledge

Calculators and computers have taken much of the drudgery out of math, but they cannot replace the number sense that is learned in the process of mastering many of the fundamental concepts, facts, and skills of basic arithmetic.

Mathematics is made of 50 percent formulas, 50 percent proofs, and 50 percent imagination.

K.I.S.S.
The Mathnasium Teaching Principle:
Kept It Short and Simple